This *Walker* book
belongs to:

For Emma
and Joe, Naomi, Eddie, Laura, Isaac, Elsie and Emile.

And for all the doctors, nurses, physiotherapists,
occupational therapists and hospital workers who saved my life
and have helped me get better.

M.R.

First published 2021 by Walker Books Ltd
87 Vauxhall Walk, London SE11 5HJ

This edition published 2022

2 4 6 8 10 9 7 5 3 1

Text © 2021 Michael Rosen
Illustrations © 2021 Tony Ross

The right of Michael Rosen and Tony Ross to be identified as author
and illustrator respectively of this work has been asserted in
accordance with the Copyright, Designs and Patents Act 1988

This book has been typeset in Bookman

Printed in China

British Library Cataloguing in Publication
Data: a catalogue record for this book is
available from the British Library

ISBN 978-1-5295-0324-1

www.walker.co.uk

Michael Rosen's STICKY McSTICKSTICK

The Friend Who Helped Me Walk Again

Michael Rosen

illustrated by

Tony Ross

WALKER BOOKS
AND SUBSIDIARIES
LONDON • BOSTON • SYDNEY • AUCKLAND

I was ill.
I was so ill I couldn't get up.

One day, three people came to my bedside
and said, "Today we're going to get you up."

They lifted me up,
one on one side,
one on the other,
one behind.

I gasped.
I panted.
My legs were shaking.

I pleaded with them to let me get back into bed.
"Please let me go back to bed!"

They let me.

The next day
they came to my bedside again
and said, "We're going to get you up."

I gasped and panted.

They put a frame in front of me
and asked me to hold it.

I did.

I was still gasping and panting.
I held on to the frame.

They said, "See if you can move the frame forwards."

I did.

Just a tiny bit.

But I gasped and panted some more.
And they put me back to bed.

The next day, they said that I should see if I could get
from the frame to a wheelchair.

All three of them helped me.

We did it.

I liked the wheelchair.
I wheeled round the room
and the corridors.

I looked out the window.

It was the first time I had seen outside
for two months.
I saw a man go into his house.
I saw cars pass.
I saw a woman come out and water her flowers
on her balcony.

They put me back to bed after that.

The next day
they said we were going to the gym.
The gym?!

First on the frame,
then in the wheelchair,
then off to the gym!

At the gym,
they said they were going to teach me how to stand up by myself.
They said, "Hands behind! Nose over toes!"

And I did it!

The next day they said they were going to teach me how to walk between parallel bars.

They did.

The next day they said they were going to teach me how to play
football between the parallel bars.

They did.

And we played with a balloon,
kicking it to and fro.

I learned how to walk down the corridor using the frame.

A few days later,
they said that I had to give up the frame.
I had to use a stick.

I was scared.
I thought I would fall over.
I called my stick
"Sticky McStickstick".

I loved Sticky McStickstick.
He helped me walk:

move the right leg,
stick down on the right,
move the left leg.

Stick down on the right,
move the left leg,
move the right leg.

Over and over again.

Then they said that
I had to learn how to climb the stairs.

I was gasping and panting all over again.

The stairs were the hardest thing of all.

But now I could walk about the corridor
with Sticky McStickstick.

One day a man came and said
that I was using the stick too much.
I had to learn how to walk without a stick.

So I tried it.

One step.

Then two steps.

Then three steps.

I was afraid that I would fall over.

But I didn't.

I thought I would try to walk from my bed
to the toilet without Sticky McStickstick.
Very, very slowly – I did!
I did it!
I was very, very proud that I had done that
all by myself.

I looked back at Sticky McStickstick
by my bed.

I felt that I had deserted him.

Then one day they came to my bed
and said that I was going home.

I asked if I could take Sticky McStickstick with me.
Yes, that was OK.

When I got home
there was my lovely family!

Everyone watched to see if I could climb the stairs.

I could!

They watched to see if I could get to the toilet by myself.

I could!

They watched to see if I could make a cup of tea.

I could!

Sticky McStickstick watched me too.
But sometimes he played hide-and-seek.

It was wonderful being home
with my family.

I practised walking round the garden.
I practised walking to the shops.
I did mini squats and stretches.

I can climb the stairs
without holding the banister.

I can make a cup of tea
without leaning on the cupboards.

I can walk to the park to meet up with my son,
his wife and my granddaughter.

I can do all these things now.

Sticky McStickstick sits in the basket by the front door
just in case I need him.

I often look at him, on the way out,
thinking of the time when he helped me
to learn how to walk.

And he reminds me of the kind people
who taught me all those things
right from the time
I couldn't even stand up.

In March 2020, I became very ill with Covid. I got so ill that they had to put me to sleep for 40 days. That's a long time doing nothing. It's so long that when I woke up I found that my arms and legs had stopped working. I couldn't stand up. I couldn't walk. Then, bit by bit the wonderful people in our hospitals taught me how to do these things. When I think about this, I think it's amazing.

My best friend became my stick. I learned how to use the stick properly and it helped me walk again … until … until a day came when I didn't need it any more.

Maybe you've been ill. Or maybe you know someone who's been ill. When we're ill, we change, don't we? And then we do what we can to get better. People help us. Maybe you're someone who's helped others. Sometimes we get fed up and sad about these things. I find that writing about it helps me. It cheers me up. Sometimes reading about these things helps me too.

I hope this book will give you a chance to think and talk about trying to get better. Maybe you'll write about it too.

M.R.

Also from Michael Rosen:

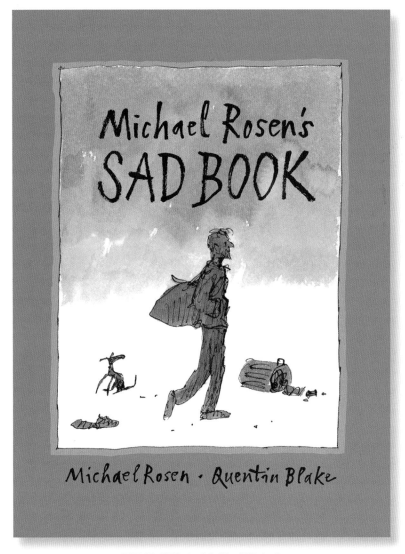

ISBN 978-1-4063-1784-8

Available from all good booksellers